The Galloway Chilli

Written & Illustrated

By

Shalla Gray

Curlytale Books

For Sheena Horner

the Galloway Chilli lady

The chilli looked up, and saw the magpie

landing beside her, a glint in his eye.

That's very kind of you!

the wee chilli said

You're welcome!

Said the magpie; "Climb on to my head!"

The magpie's beak snapped the poor chilli in two!

But his mouth went on fire when he started to chew.

As she fell through the air, the chilli spun round and round;

scattering Galloway Chilli seeds over the ground.

So even though the Galloway Chilli was gone,
through her baby chilli plants, her memory lives on!

Also from Curly Tale Books:

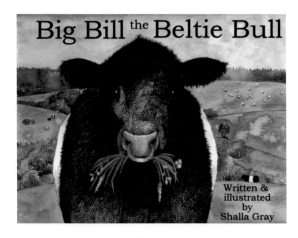

And also by Shalla Gray;

About the Author

Shalla lives in a wee village in rural Galloway, where she runs the Post Office & Shop with her partner Steve and their four children. She is also a director of Curly Tale Books with her writer friend Jayne Baldwin. Shalla loves to paint and draw to relax, and it was writing and illustrating bedtime stories for her children which led to the publication of her books.

The story of The Galloway Chilli was inspired by Galloway Chillies' Chilli Jam; of which the author is a big fan!

This picture shows Shalla posing beside her 'Beltie Beach Hut' on a sunny day in Kirkcudbright.

© Curly Tale Books 2014

ISBN 978-0-9576402-3-8

Published by

Curly Tale Books Ltd

34 Main Street

Kirkcowan

DG8 0HG

www.curlytalebooks.co.uk

check out our facebook page, or follow us on twitter Curly Tale Books

Written and Illustrated

By

Shalla Gray

PRINTED BY

J&B Print, 32A Albert St., Newton Stewart, DG8 6EJ

Special thanks to Sheena of Galloway Chillies

www.gallowaychillies.co.uk

 P.S. There's a friendly wee ant hiding on every page – can you see him?